Marco Ma[...]

He's a joker who [...]
messing about, [...]
always means w[...]
if he sometimes [...]
things wrong.

Philippa Feltpen

A real peacemaker, she
helps keep the other
Pens in order by sorting
out arguments and giving
good advice.

Waxy Max

He's very sporty and
football mad. On the
outside, he's tough,
but underneath he's
got the biggest heart.

What's this lot
going to be up
to this month?

Squiggle and Splodge

The Scribble twins! They're
both quiet, both shy.
Although they may not
look alike, they do almost
everything together.

Enter ...

Squiggle, what's a friend?

I don't know Splodge. I hope they tell us inside ..

Pens

Helping you to get to know God more

Friends

Written by

Alexa Tewkesbury

Every day a short Bible reading is brought to life with the help of the Pens characters. A related question and prayer apply this to daily life. Written in four sections, two focusing on the lives of Pens and two on Bible characters, young children will be inspired to learn more of God and His Word.

What's inside?

Being a Friend — Day 1

Everybody's Friend – The story of Zacchaeus — Day 11

Daddy God — Day 16

God's Promise – Abraham and Sarah have a baby — Day 26

CWR

FSC

Mixed Sources
Product group from well-managed
forests and other controlled sources
www.fsc.org Cert no. SGS-COC-003963
© 1996 Forest Stewardship Council

'When someone asks you for something, give it to him; when someone wants to borrow something, lend it to him.' (Matthew 5 v 42)

The special hat

Gloria! I'm going somewhere special, and I need a special hat. Could I borrow one, please?

You can borrow whichever one you like.

Philippa chose a hat with swirly feathers.

4

The next day, Gloria went to get a biscuit, but the tin was empty.

'Bother,' she said. 'I just fancy a biscuit.'

Philippa knocked at the door.

'It was so kind of you to lend me your hat,' she smiled. 'To say thank you, I've brought you some biscuits.'

 Jesus likes us to share what we have with others.

What do you have that you could share with your friends?

Pens Prayer

Thank You, Lord Jesus, for everything You give me. May I always be ready to lend and to share. Amen.

5

Day 2   Being a Friend

'… be kind … to one another, and forgive one another, as God has forgiven you …' (Ephesians 4 v 32)

Charlotte's softer song

Charlotte was singing. Loudly. She sang high. She sang low. She warbled about in the middle. Denzil was cross.

6

'You've been singing for hours,' he groaned. 'You're giving me a headache.'

'But I love singing,' Charlotte trilled. 'It makes me happy.'

'It's making *me* miserable,' moaned Denzil.

Charlotte looked upset. Before long, Denzil was looking upset too.

'Please don't stop singing,' he said. 'I'm sorry I was grumpy.'

Charlotte smiled. 'That's all right, Denzil. And just for you, I'll try and sing more quietly.'

If God can forgive us for the wrong things we do, then we should also try to forgive each other.

If you do something wrong, what is it good to remember to say?

Pens Prayer

Please, Lord, help me to be able to forgive other people if they are unkind to me, just as You always forgive me if I make You unhappy. Amen.

Day 3 — Being a Friend

'Do not forget to do good and to help one another ...' (Hebrews 13 v 16)

Philippa's **smile**

'Gloria, please help me bake a cake,' said Denzil.

'Certainly,' answered Gloria. 'What kind of cake?'

'A cheering-someone-up cake,' said Denzil. 'Philippa's lost her smile and I want to help her find it.'

So they beat and mixed, and stirred and whisked, and the cake looked delicious.

'Philippa,' said Denzil, 'we've made you a cake to help you find your smile.'

Philippa was surprised … then pleased … then, suddenly …

'It's back!' laughed Gloria.

And there it was, a huge smile right across Philippa's face.

 Taking time to cheer up our friends makes Jesus happy, too.

What could you do to cheer up someone who is sad?

Pens Prayer

Lord Jesus, You are always ready to comfort me when I'm sad. May I always be ready to comfort people, too. Amen.

9

Day 4 — Being a Friend

'Do everything without complaining or arguing ...'
(Philippians 2 v 14)

Sharpy's bath

Sharpy was very muddy.

'You'll have to give him a bath, Max,' said Gloria.

'Why me?' frowned Max.

'Because I hate mud,' Gloria replied.

'Please help me,' said Max. 'It'll be fun.'

Gloria wrinkled her nose. 'All right,' she moaned. 'But there's nothing funny about mud.'

They washed and they scrubbed, and when Sharpy was spotless, they dried him with Gloria's hairdryer.

'Beautiful,' smiled Gloria.

'Cool,' agreed Max.

'You were right,' added Gloria. 'That *was* fun. I'll always help you when Sharpy needs a bath.'

 Working cheerfully with our friends is good for them, and for us, too.

What do you enjoy doing with your friends?

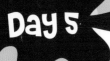

'I was sick and you took care of me ...' (Matthew 25 v 36)

A croak in the throat

Charlotte's throat was so sore she couldn't sing, and singing's what Charlotte enjoyed most.

What's up?

It's my throat. It's so sore I can't sing.

'Oh, dear,' replied Max.

'Perhaps,' suggested Charlotte, 'if *you* sang to *me*, it might get better more quickly.'

'Oh, dear,' Max said again. 'I'm not good at singing. But we could play with my football instead.'

'No, thank you,' whispered Charlotte.

'All right,' smiled Max, 'if it'll help you get better, singing it is.'

 Looking after each other shows our love for our friends and for Jesus.

How many ways can you think of to show a sick friend that you care?

Pens Prayer

Thank You, Lord, for caring about me when I'm ill. Please show me how I can care for other people. Amen.

Day 6 — Being a Friend

'Do not use harmful words, but only helpful words, the kind that build up and provide what is needed, so that what you say will do good to those who hear you.' (Ephesians 4 v 29)

Gloria's first slide

'Wheee!' shrieked Marco, shooting down the slide.

'Wahaay!' screeched Max, whizzing down behind him.

'Oooh,' quivered Gloria. 'I can't go on the slide. It's too high. I might fall off.'

'Of course you won't,' said Marco kindly.

'You can do it, we know you can,' encouraged Max.

So slowly, very slowly, and carefully, very carefully, Gloria climbed to the top of the slide and – 'Wooo!' – zoomed all the way down.

'Hooray!' yelled Max and Marco, and Gloria beamed happily, from ear to ear.

 Jesus was careful to use kind words when He spoke to people.

Who do you know who has been kind to you? Say thank you to them this week.

Pens Prayer

Thank You, Lord, for kind words that make me smile. Help me to remember to speak kindly to my friends to encourage them. Amen.

Day 7 — Being a Friend

'Remember those who are suffering, as though you were suffering as they are.' (Hebrews 13 v 3)

Sharpy saves the day

Marco was worried.

'Oh no,' he moaned. 'Oh no, oh no, OH NO.'

'What's wrong?' asked Philippa. 'You look very worried.'

'It's Max's football,' replied Marco worriedly. 'He lent it to me and I kicked it into the pond. He's going to be so cross.'

'That's nothing to worry about,' smiled Philippa. 'Sharpy's good at swimming. He can fetch it.'

So Sharpy jumped into the pond and brought the ball back.

'Oh, thank you!' beamed Marco – and he didn't need to be worried any more.

 Jesus likes us to help each other when we're in trouble.

Who can you ask for help when you're sad or worried?

Pens Prayer

Dear Lord Jesus, may I always be ready to help someone who needs me. Amen.

Being a Friend

'… our love should not be just words and talk; it must be true love, which shows itself in action.' (1 John 3 v 18)

Charlotte's new friends

When Charlotte first saw Squiggle and Splodge, she wasn't sure she was going to like them.

They're different from us.

We're all different from each other, but we ALL need friends.

So Charlotte and Philippa went to say hello. Squiggle and Splodge were so pleased to meet them that the four of them chatted away all afternoon.

'Thank you for making us feel so welcome,' smiled Squiggle.

'Oh no,' said Charlotte, 'thank *you* for being such lovely new friends.'

When we welcome people who are new to us, we show them Jesus' love.

Do you know someone who needs a friend?

Pens Prayer

I thank You, Jesus, for the times when I can make new friends. Amen.

19

Being a Friend

'Your God, the LORD himself, will be with you. He will not fail you or abandon you.' (Deuteronomy 31 v 6)

marco's surprise

Marco wanted to surprise Gloria, so he decided to paint the flowers on her hat. He painted the red flowers blue and the yellow ones purple.

But the paint made the petals soggy, and the colours ran and looked like mud.

'Marco!' squealed Gloria. 'What *have* you done?'

'Don't be cross, Gloria,' said Philippa. 'Marco might have made a mess, but he meant to be kind.'

'He's ruined my hat,' Gloria wailed.

'Maybe a little,' replied Philippa, 'but he was trying to be a good friend.'

 It's important for friends to stand up for each other.

How can you be kind to your friends?

Pens Prayer

Lord Jesus, thank You for my friends. Please help me to be loyal to them, just as You are loyal to me. Amen.

Pens were having a party to say thank You to their very best Friend because He loved them so much. He was amazing. He always had time to listen to them. He was always ready to help them. He always forgave them when they did things wrong, and He never went away. Pens' best Friend was always, ALWAYS there.

When everything was ready, Denzil said, 'Right, Pens, after three – one, two, three ...'

Then – 'Thank You, Jesus!' they all shouted together, and everyone cheered VERY loudly.

Jesus wants to be our best Friend for ever and ever.

What can you thank Jesus for right now?

Pens Prayer

Thank You, Jesus, for being so wonderful. I never want to forget how much You've done for me. Amen.

23

EVERYBODY'S FRIEND
The story of Zacchaeus

Day 11

'Zacchaeus … was a little man and could not see Jesus because of the crowd.' (Luke 19 vv 2–3)

Zacchaeus and the crowd

Nobody liked greedy Zacchaeus because he took money from people. One day, Jesus came to town. Zacchaeus was only a little man and couldn't see Jesus over the heads of the crowd who went to meet Him. 'Serves him right,' the people said. 'A greedy man like that doesn't deserve to meet Jesus.'

Zacchaeus did bad things but he still wanted to see Jesus.

Is there someone special you'd like to meet?

Pens Prayer

Dear Lord Jesus, I may only be little like Zacchaeus, but please help me to remember that whenever I want to talk to You, You are always ready to listen. Amen.

Day 12

'... [Zacchaeus] ran ahead ... and climbed a sycomore tree to see Jesus ... [Jesus] looked up and said ... "Hurry down, Zacchaeus, because I must stay in your house today."' (Luke 19 vv 4–5)

A **Surprise** for **Zacchaeus**

Zacchaeus thought no one would notice him hidden in the tree, but Jesus knew he was there. Jesus also knew how much everyone hated Zacchaeus because of the bad things he did. But Jesus didn't hate him. He wanted to be Zacchaeus's friend.

Jesus loved Zacchaeus even though no one else liked him.

What do you enjoy doing with your friends?

Pens Prayer

Thank You, Jesus, that You know me from my head to my toes, and that You love me from my toes to my head. Amen.

Everybody's Friend
The story of Zacchaeus

Day 13

'Zacchaeus hurried down and welcomed [Jesus] with great joy. All the people … started grumbling, "This man has gone as a guest to the home of a sinner!"' (Luke 19 vv 6–7)

Jesus makes Zaccheus happy

When the people saw Jesus going into Zacchaeus's house, they were cross. Zacchaeus was a greedy man and a cheat, and they thought Jesus should have nothing to do with him.

Jesus didn't mind what people thought. What He cared about was making friends with Zacchaeus.

Pens Prayer

Dear Lord Jesus, please help me to be kind to people the way You were to Zacchaeus, because everyone needs kindness. Amen.

Everybody's Friend
The story of Zacchaeus

Day 14

'Zacchaeus stood up and said to the Lord, "Listen, sir! I will give half my belongings to the poor, and if I have cheated anyone, I will pay back four times as much."' (Luke 19 v 8)

Zacchaeus is sorry

Zacchaeus was so happy to have Jesus as his Friend that he was sorry for being greedy and unkind. He decided to give a lot of his things away to people who were poor, and to pay back all the money he had taken.

 Jesus showed Zacchaeus how to be good and kind.

How could you be kind to someone today?

Pens Prayer

I'm sorry for the bad things I sometimes do, Lord Jesus. Help me to try to be good for You every day. Amen.

Everybody's Friend
The story of Zacchaeus

Day 15

'Jesus said to [Zacchaeus], "Salvation has come to this house today ... The Son of Man came to seek and to save the lost."' (Luke 19 vv 9–10)

Jesus wants to be everyone's Friend

Jesus didn't just want to make friends with people who tried to be good and kind. He wanted to be a Friend to everyone, no matter what they were like or what they'd done wrong. And Jesus wants to be your Friend today.

When Jesus finds a new friend, it makes Him very happy.

Do you have a best friend?

Pens Prayer

Dear Lord Jesus, thank You for being my special Friend. When I see people who are shy or sad or lonely, I want to be a friend to them – just as You are to me. Amen.

'This God – how perfect are his deeds!' (Psalm 18 v 30)

The perfect day

It was Saturday morning, and Pens all woke up in a very good mood.

'Lovely,' said Gloria happily.
'What a perfect day for shopping!'

'Brilliant,' said Max excitedly.
'What a perfect day for football!'

'Super,' said Charlotte cheerfully.
'What a perfect day for singing!'

'Wow,' said Marco brightly.
'What a perfect day for swimming!'

'Gorgeous,' said Philippa chirpily.
'What a perfect day for gardening!'

'Cool,' said Denzil smoothly.
'What a perfect day for cycling!'

'After all,' added Gloria, 'some days are just perfect for doing whatever you want.'

God is perfect every day
– in every way.

How would you spend your perfect day?

Pens Prayer

Please hold my hand, Father God, and keep me close to You through everything I say and everything I do. Amen.

35

Day 17 — Daddy God

'Praise the LORD, my soul, and do not forget how kind he is.' (Psalm 103 v 2)

Gloria's too late

Bus Stop

Gloria was catching the bus.

'Which hat shall I wear?' she wondered.

She spent ages choosing.

'The red one …? No, the green … Although, I do fancy the purple … But my blue one's very pretty … And I so *love* the yellow …'

Finally, Gloria chose her pink hat. But she took so long, she missed the bus.

'Bother,' she moaned.

'What's "bother"?' asked Marco.

'I've missed the bus.'

Marco smiled kindly. 'I'll wait with you. Keep you company till the next one comes.'

 When we're kind to each other, God is pleased because He loves being kind to us, too.

How many different ways could you travel from place to place?

Pens Prayer

Lord God, please help me to be like You – always kind and ready to be a good friend. Amen.

The sun was shining. The sky was blue. It was a beautiful day.

'Definitely a day,' Charlotte said, 'for a picnic.'

'Good idea,' agreed Denzil.

They packed sandwiches and drinks, and some perfectly picnic-sized cakes.

But grey clouds began to shuffle across the sun and, soon, big, wet raindrops plopped and splashed onto the ground.

Philippa arrived.

'Come under my umbrella,' she said. 'We can all keep dry under here.'

They kept the food dry, too. And when the rain stopped, they all enjoyed the picnic together.

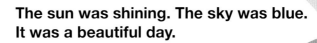 God wants to look after us every day.

What do you like to do on rainy days?

Pens Prayer

When things go wrong and are difficult, please take care of me so that I can feel safe knowing You are with me. Amen.

Day 19
Daddy God

'He forgives all my sins …' (Psalm 103 v 3)

max's new boot

Max loved his new football boot. It was BRILLIANT for kicking.

Sharpy loved it, too – but not so much for football.

What Sharpy loved it for was chewing. It was perfect. Bendy but tough – just right for getting his sharp teeth into.

'Sharpy!' shouted Max. 'What have you *done*?'

'Whoops,' thought Sharpy, and he scurried off to hide.

When Max saw how sorry Sharpy was, he couldn't stay angry forever.

'That was very naughty. That was my best boot,' he said. 'But I forgive you. Come on out.'

 When we are sorry for doing something wrong, God is always ready to forgive us.

Have you ever needed to forgive someone who's done something wrong?

Pens Prayer

Lord God, it's hard to be good all the time, but thank You so much that You forgive me for the bad times and love me anyway. Amen.

41

Daddy God

'... in all things you are faithful, O LORD.' (Psalm 89 v 8)

Scaredy Splodge

'Oh, dear,' murmured Splodge. 'Oh, no …'

She stood up. She sat down. She went outside. She came back in. She even ate a banana. Nothing helped.

'Do I have to?' she muttered.

'Do you have to what?' asked Squiggle.

'It's just …' Splodge began … 'You see …' she went on … 'What I mean is … we're starting at our new school tomorrow and I'm scared.'

'Silly!' smiled Squiggle. 'We'll be going together. And I promise I'll never leave you.'

'Never?' asked Splodge.

'Never,' replied Squiggle.

When we need Him, God is always there.

What can you do if you ever feel afraid?

Pens Prayer

Thank You, Father God, that when I'm worried or afraid, You're always right beside me. Amen.

Day 21   Daddy God

'He fills my life with good things ...' (Psalm 103 v 5)

marco's sunflower

44

Marco found something.

'What's this?' he asked.

'A sunflower seed, I think,' answered Philippa.

'How can I make it grow?' Marco went on.

'You have to give it what it needs,' replied Philippa.

She put soil in a pot, and Marco pushed the seed down into it.

'It needs water, too,' added Philippa, 'and some sunshine.'

After a few days, out of the pot sprang a little green shoot.

'You were right,' grinned Marco. 'We gave the seed everything it needed, and now it's growing!'

 God knows how to care for us by giving us what's best.

What do you need to help you grow?

Pens Prayer

Lord God, I thank You that though You may not always give me what I want, You always give me what I need. Amen.

45

Day 22 — Daddy God

'Great and mighty is our Lord …' (Psalm 147 v 5)

Is it a monster?

Something was roaring …
Something was growling …
Something was howling …

Sharpy shot under the bed,
Denzil dived behind the sofa,
and Squiggle and Splodge tried
to hide behind each other.

'Is it a m-m-monster?' everyone stammered.

'No!' laughed Charlotte. 'It's just the wind.'

Outside, trees were waving, hedges were rocking, and leaves were whizzing through the air.

'Wow!' shrieked Splodge. 'The wind must be very powerful to do ALL THAT!'

'I knew it was the wind, really,' said Denzil.

'Of course you did,' smiled Charlotte.

 The wind is strong, but God's power is SO HUGE that He was able to make the whole world.

What is your favourite kind of weather?

Pens Prayer

How wonderful You are, dear Father God, because although You are mighty enough to create the world, You wanted to make me, too. Amen.

Day 23 — Daddy God

'The LORD is loving and merciful, slow to become angry and full of constant love.' (Psalm 145 v 8)

Keeping cool

Gloria was gardening. THWACK! A football landed in her sweet peas.

Sorry I hit your flowers ...

'I've dug up your weeds,' announced Charlotte.

'No!' cried Gloria.
'They're my best flowers.'

'Oops,' said Charlotte.

Never mind. They still look beautiful.

'I'll plant some more,' Gloria sighed. Then –

'Sharpy!' she called.
'What *are* you doing?'

Sharpy was digging in the lawn. He gave Gloria a wet, tickly lick. Gloria laughed.

'You're very patient today,' remarked Charlotte.

'I hate being cross with my friends,' smiled Gloria.

 God is patient with us when we get things wrong and helps us to try again.

Do you sometimes find it hard to be patient?

Pens Prayer

Thank You, Lord, that You are patient enough to forgive me not just once, but over and over again. Amen.

49

Day 24   Daddy God

'The LORD is king for ever.' (Psalm 146 v 10)

Charlotte's House

Denzil's different day

Denzil was thoughtful.

'I've been thinking,' he said. 'At the shop, a different man from usual was behind the counter. At the library, a different lady from usual took my books. At the dentist, a different dentist from usual looked at my teeth. At Charlotte's house, her front door had been painted a different colour from usual. *And* she'd changed her curtains and they had a different pattern. So what I've been thinking is … *nothing* stays the same.'

'God does,' smiled Philippa. 'He's the same every day.'

 Today, tomorrow and always – God's love for us never changes.

How can you remember God every day?

Pens Prayer

Heavenly Father, when things change all around me, You are still the King of the whole world. Please be King in my life always, too. Amen.

51

Day 25 — Daddy God

'His love is so great that we are called God's children ...'
(1 John 3 v 1)

Where's Sharpy?

Where's Sharpy?

Don't know. Is he with Marco?

52

'No,' shrugged Waxy Max. 'Is he with Philippa?'

'No,' frowned Philippa. 'Is he with Gloria?'

'No,' said Gloria.

'So where is he?' worried Charlotte.

Pens searched everywhere. All afternoon. They wouldn't give up … until finally –

'Found you!' shrieked Max.

Sharpy had fallen into a dustbin.

'You're safe now,' beamed Charlotte. 'We love you too much to let you stay lost forever.'

 God loves His children so much that He will never let us go.

Pens Prayer

How amazing, Father God, that wherever I am and whatever I'm doing, You are always with me. Thank You for being my Heavenly Daddy. Amen.

GOD'S PROMISE
Abraham and Sarah have a baby

Day 26

'... the LORD appeared to [Abraham] and said, "I am the Almighty God. Obey me and always do what is right."' (Genesis 17 v 1)

Friends forever

Abraham was God's friend. Whenever God wanted to speak to him, he was always ready to listen. Abraham knew that God loved him and wanted the best for him, so he tried as hard as he could to do as God asked.

Abraham was happy to obey God because he trusted Him.

How could you make God happy today?

Pens Prayer

Teach me, Lord God, to listen to You and to live as You want me to day by day. Amen.

God's Promise
Abraham and Sarah have a baby

Day 27

'God said to Abraham, "… I will give you a son …"'
(Genesis 17 vv 15–16)

A **Present** for **Abraham**

56

Abraham and his wife Sarah were sad because they didn't have any children. But Abraham was such a special friend to God that God promised to give him and Sarah a baby boy. And that wasn't all. 'One day,' God said, 'you will have as many grandchildren and great-grandchildren as there are stars in the sky!'

God wanted to give Abraham a present because He was pleased with him.

What makes you happy?

Pens Prayer

Dear Lord God, when I am sad, please help me to remember that You love me and want to fill my life with good things. Amen.

God's Promise
Abraham and Sarah have a baby

Day 28

'... but [Abraham] began to laugh when he thought, "Can a man have a child when he is a hundred years old? Can Sarah have a child at ninety?"' (Genesis 17 v 17)

Too **good** to be **true**

Abraham and Sarah wanted a baby of their own very much, but they were old – much too old to have children, Abraham thought. He loved and trusted God but this promise was just a little too hard to believe.

Abraham needed to learn that God always means what He says.

Why is it important to keep the promises you make?

Pens Prayer

Father God, please teach me that I can trust in You completely every day. Amen.

God's Promise
Abraham and Sarah have a baby

Day 29

'Then the LORD asked Abraham, "… Is anything too hard for the LORD?"' (Genesis 18 vv 13–14)

Sarah's giggle

It wasn't just Abraham who laughed when God said He would give him a son. Sarah laughed, too. 'At my age?' she chuckled. 'It's impossible.' God heard what she said but He took no notice. He knew what He was going to do.

 God wanted to show Abraham and Sarah that nothing is impossible for Him.

What can you do when you find something difficult?

Pens Prayer

Dear Lord, it's amazing that what seems impossible for me is possible for You. Help me to believe in Your promises always. Amen.

God's Promise
Abraham and Sarah have a baby

Day 30

'The LORD blessed Sarah, as he had promised ...'
(Genesis 21 v 1)

God keeps His promise

62

When Abraham and Sarah's baby son was born, there were huge, beaming smiles all over their faces. 'I shall call you Isaac,' Abraham said to the little boy. Someone else was smiling that day, too. It was God. He'd given Abraham and Sarah a wonderful present, just as He said He would.

When God makes a promise, He keeps it.

Have you ever made a promise to someone?

Pens Prayer

Lord God, thank You so much that when You make a promise, You mean it. May I always mean the promises I make to You, too. Amen.

Other Pens titles

Visit www.cwr.org.uk for list of
National Distributors.

All Scripture references are from the GNB:
Good News Bible © 1996, 1971, 1976
American Bible Society.

Concept development, editing, design
and production by CWR

Printed in China by 1010 Printing Ltd.

ISBN: 978-1-85345-554-4

OTHER CWR DAILY BIBLE-READING NOTES
Every Day with Jesus for adults
Inspiring Women Every Day for women
Lucas on Life Every Day for adults
Cover to Cover Every Day for adults
Mettle for 14- to 18-year-olds
YP's for 11- to 15-year-olds
Topz for 7- to 11-year-olds